CHANNELS ONLY

ARR. © COPYRIGHT, 1963, BY THE RODEHEAVER CO., IN "SCHULER'S PIANO-ORGAN DUETS NO. 2"
INTERNATIONAL COPYRIGHT SECURED   ALL RIGHTS RESERVED

ADA ROSE GIBBS
Arr. George S. Schuler

CHANNELS ONLY

CHANNELS ONLY

OVERSHADOWED

COPYRIGHT, 1935, RENEWAL, 1963, THE RODEHEAVER CO., OWNER
© COPYRIGHT, 1963, BY THE RODEHEAVER CO., IN SCHULER'S PIANO-ORGAN DUETS NO. 2"
INTERNATIONAL COPYRIGHT SECURED   ALL RIGHTS RESERVED

GEORGE S. SCHULER
Arr. George S. Schuler

OVERSHADOWED

OVERSHADOWED

IN THE GARDEN

© COPYRIGHT, 1912, RENEWAL, 1940, THE RODEHEAVER CO., OWNER
© COPYRIGHT, 1963, BY THE RODEHEAVER CO. IN "SCHULER'S PIANO-ORGAN DUETS NO. 2"
INTERNATIONAL COPYRIGHT SECURED ALL RIGHTS RESERVED

C. AUSTIN MILES
Arr. George S. Schuler

IN THE GARDEN

IN THE GARDEN

DEEP WITHIN MY HEART

© COPYRIGHT, 1961, THE RODEHEAVER CO., OWNER
© COPYRIGHT, 1963, BY THE RODEHEAVER CO., IN "SCHULER'S PIANO – ORGAN DUETS NO. 2"
INTERNATIONAL COPYRIGHT SECURED   ALL RIGHTS RESERVED

GEORGE S. SCHULER
Arr. by George S. Schuler

DEEP WITHIN MY HEART

NEARER, STILL NEARER

ARR. © COPYRIGHT, 1963, BY THE RODEHEAVER CO., IN "SCHULER'S PIANO-ORGAN DUETS NO. 2"
INTERNATIONAL COPYRIGHT SECURED   ALL RIGHTS RESERVED

MRS. C. H. MORRIS
Arr. by George S. Schuler

NEARER, STILL NEARER

NEARER, STILL NEARER

HE IS MINE

COPYRIGHT 1912, RENEWAL, 1940, THE RODEHEAVER CO., OWNER
© COPYRIGHT, 1963, BY THE RODEHEAVER CO., IN "SCHULER'S PIANO-ORGAN DUETS NO. 2"
INTERNATIONAL COPYRIGHT SECURED   ALL RIGHTS RESERVED

J. LINCOLN HALL
Arr. George S. Schuler

HE IS MINE

HE IS MINE

HE IS MINE

18

*with nail of R.H. 2nd finger, in key of C

MY SAVIOUR'S LOVE

ARR. © COPYRIGHT, 1963, BY THE RODEHEAVER CO., IN "SCHULER'S PIANO-ORGAN DUETS NO. 2"
INTERNATIONAL COPYRIGHT SECURED ALL RIGHTS RESERVED

CHARLES H. GABRIEL
Arr. by George S. Schuler

MY SAVIOUR'S LOVE

MY SAVIOUR'S LOVE

HOPE'S GOLDEN DAY

COPYRIGHT, 1948, BY VAN KAMPEN PRESS
ASSIGNED TO THE RODEHEAVER CO.
© COPYRIGHT, 1963, BY THE RODEHEAVER CO., IN "SCHULER'S PIANO-ORGAN DUETS NO. 2"
INTERNATIONAL COPYRIGHT SECURED   ALL RIGHTS RESERVED

GEORGE S. SCHULER
Arr. by George S. Schuler

NOTE: The harmonic structure of this number is similar to the immortal music of Puccini

Hope's Golden Day

Hope's Golden Day

CONSECRATION

GEORGE S. SCHULER
Arr. by George S. Schuler

CONSECRATION

SILENT NIGHT - FIRST NOEL - MIDNIGHT CLEAR 27

ARR. © COPYRIGHT, 1963, BY THE RODEHEAVER CO., IN "SCHULER'S PIANO – ORGAN DUETS NO. 2"
INTERNATIONAL COPYRIGHT SECURED   ALL RIGHTS RESERVED

GRUBER
Traditional
WILLIS
Arr. by George S. Schuler

SILENT NIGHT - FIRST NOEL - MIDNIGHT CLEAR

SILENT NIGHT - FIRST NOEL - MIDNIGHT CLEAR

MY HOPE IS IN THEE
(THE SOLID ROCK)

COPYRIGHT, 1925, RENEWAL, 1953, THE RODEHEAVER CO., OWNER
© COPYRIGHT, 1963, BY THE RODEHEAVER CO., IN "SCHULER'S PIANO-ORGAN DUETS NO. 2"
INTERNATIONAL COPYRIGHT SECURED   ALL RIGHTS RESERVED

GEORGE S. SCHULER
Arr. by George S. Schuler

NOTE: As sung in the Billy Graham campaign in England.   A fully developed anthem is in print, Octavo No. 2253

MY HOPE IS IN THEE

MY HOPE IS IN THEE

CHRIST AROSE

ROBERT LOWRY
Arr. by George S. Schuler

CHRIST AROSE

CHRIST AROSE

*With thumb nail of R.H.

ALL HAIL, IMMANUEL

COPYRIGHT, 1910, RENEWAL, 1938, THE RODEHEAVER CO., OWNER
© COPYRIGHT, 1963, BY THE RODEHEAVER CO., IN "SCHULER'S PIANO-ORGAN DUETS NO. 2"
INTERNATIONAL COPYRIGHT SECURED ALL RIGHTS RESERVED

CHARLES H. GABRIEL
Arr. by George S. Schuler

ALL HAIL, IMMANUEL

ALL HAIL, IMMANUEL

ALL HAIL, IMMANUEL

40 STAND UP, STAND UP FOR JESUS

ARR. © COPYRIGHT, 1963, BY THE RODEHEAVER CO., IN "SCHULER'S PIANO - ORGAN DUETS NO. 2"
INTERNATIONAL COPYRIGHT SECURED ALL RIGHTS RESERVED

GEORGE J. WEBB
ADAM GEIBEL
Arr. by George S. Schuler

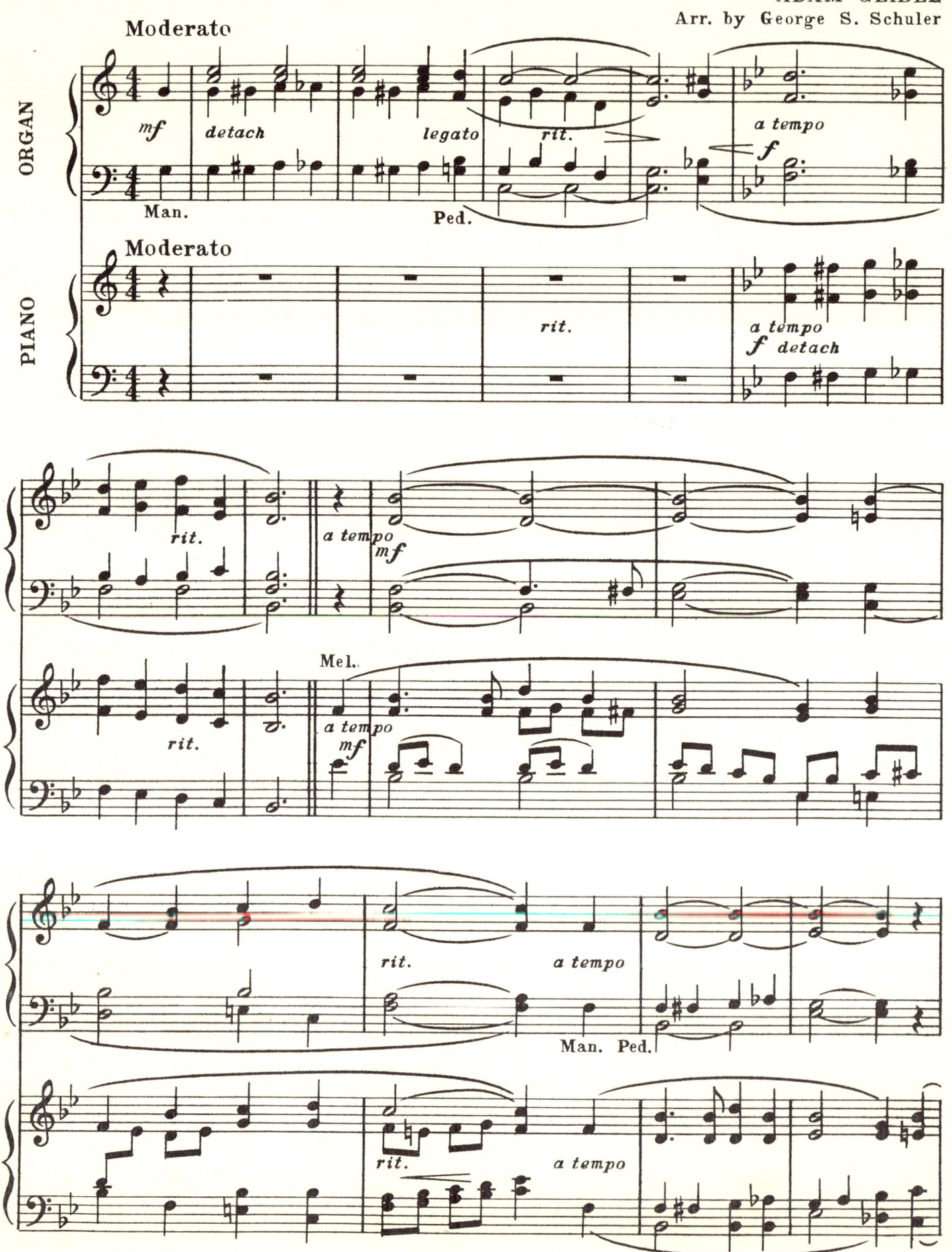

STAND UP, STAND UP FOR JESUS

STAND UP, STAND UP FOR JESUS

STAND UP, STAND FOR JESUS

THAT WILL BE GLORY

ARR. © COPYRIGHT, 1963, BY THE RODEHEAVER CO., IN "SCHULER'S PIANO-ORGAN DUETS NO. 2"
INTERNATIONAL COPYRIGHT SECURED   ALL RIGHTS RESERVED

CHARLES H. GABRIEL
Arr. by George S. Schuler

NOTE: This number is not as difficult as it appears. It will need a little more practice than usual.

THAT WILL BE GLORY

THAT WILL BE GLORY

*Detach L. H. notes.

THAT WILL BE GLORY

47

THAT WILL BE GLORY